GRAPHIC LIBRARY™

GRAPHIC SCIENCE AND ENGINEERING IN ACTION

THE **AMAZING WORK** OF

SCIENTISTS

WITH MAX AXIOM
SUPER SCIENTIST

by Agnieszka Biskup

illustrated by Marcelo Baez

Raintree

Raintree is an imprint of Capstone Global Library Limited, a company incorporated in England and Wales having its registered office at 7 Pilgrim Street, London, EC4V 6LB – Registered company number: 6695582

To contact Raintree please phone 0845 6044371, fax + 44 (0) 1865 312263, or email myorders@ raintreepublishers.co.uk. Customers from outside the UK please telephone +44 1865 312262.

First published by Capstone Press in 2013
First published in the United Kingdom in 2014
The moral rights of the proprietor have been asserted.

Editor
Mari Bolte

Designer
Ted Williams

Media Researcher
Wanda Winch

Production Specialist
Laura Manthe

Originated by Capstone Global Library Ltd
Printed and bound in China by LEO Paper Products Ltd

ISBN 978 1 406 26683 2
17 16 15 14 13
10 9 8 7 6 5 4 3 2 1

A full catalogue record for this book is available from the British Library.

CONTENTS

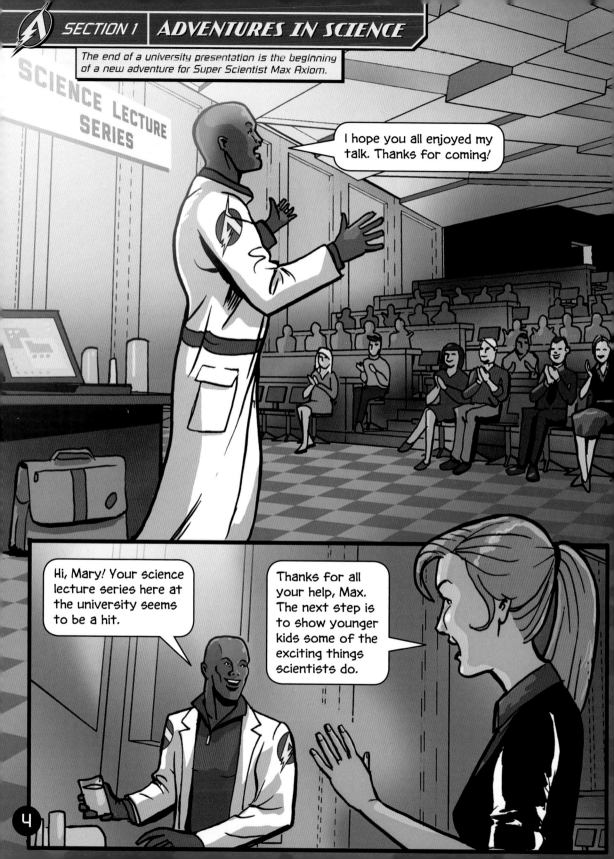

That's great! How can I help?

We're putting together a fair where children can meet real scientists face-to-face. But we need the scientists to sign up first!

No problem. Science is a huge field and I know scientists who work in the most incredible conditions.

Do you think you can spread the word about the fair?

Of course! Children will get to hear the questions scientists ask about our world. Then they can learn about the different methods each scientist uses to find the answers.

And they will see that there's more to science than labs, computers, and white coats.

That's right! Although sometimes science includes all those, too.

I'll get in touch with my friends straight away.

Thanks again, Max.

THE *ISS*

Many nations worked together to build the *ISS*. The station orbits about 402 kilometres (250 miles) above Earth. It is the largest and longest inhabited object to ever circle the planet.

The *ISS* is the world's only orbiting science laboratory. Looks like my rocket is ready for lift-off.

VROOOSSH!

Scientists do all sorts of research at the station. There's a lot to study in space!

Hi, Max! How's the *ISS* treating you?

I'm still getting used to being weightless!

Tell me more about what physiologists do in space, Amy.

I study how the lack of gravity causes muscle and bone to waste away. It's important to figure out the right type and amount of exercise to stay healthy in space.

There's lots of other research being done here, too. We have a botanist and an astronomer.

I'm studying how plants use gravity to decide which direction to grow. Children back on Earth are doing the same thing. Their seeds will be the control group.

I'm following a solar storm and recording how it affects Earth's magnetic field.

Thanks for the tour. Children at the fair will love seeing your work!

Growing astronauts?

Scientists have found that people "grow" a few centimetres taller in space. The lack of gravity causes their spines to stretch. Once they're back on Earth, gravity pulls on their backbones again. They return to their normal heights.

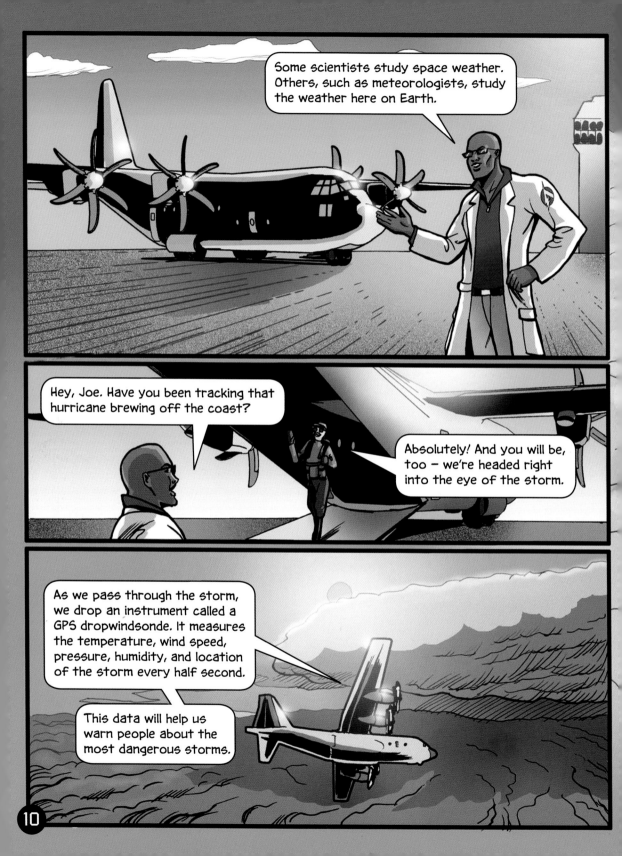

Let me help you with that. I've got some protective gear for you. It's dangerous up here.

That must be Roberto.

I'm taking gas samples today. The amount and types of gas may indicate an eruption is about to happen.

And the earlier the warning, the more time people have to evacuate.

Be careful – even the best protective suit won't protect you from lava. That pool of molten rock is over 1000 degrees Celsius!

I'm not the only scientist studying this volcano. Lee is a seismologist, which means he studies earthquakes.

I'm placing seismometers around the volcano. These instruments detect movement in Earth's crust. The movement may mean that magma is rising beneath an awakening volcano.

This information helps scientists predict when the volcano is going to erupt.

My next meeting is with a microbiologist named Anita. She's studying bacteria in caves around the island.

I'm off to survey the lava flow from the air. I'll give you a lift.

Hi, Anita! I'm ready to do some cave exploring!

Great! I've got some caving gear for you to change into. You're definitely going to need some knee pads.

Deep inside a cave, there's no sunlight and very little food. Looks like a tough place to live.

It certainly is. The bacteria that live here compete fiercely to survive. They've developed chemicals to defend themselves and fight off competitors.

These chemicals could help us make new drugs to fight cancer and other diseases.

Who knows what other useful stuff might be discovered from this sample of bacteria?

Looks like your lift is waiting!

See you at the fair!

Ready to visit the bottom of the sea?

Absolutely, Jill. Not that long ago people thought nothing lived at the bottom of the ocean.

But thanks to deep-sea submersibles like this one, marine scientists have discovered a world full of life.

For instance, scientists discovered hot thermal vents and the animals that live around them.

We've also discovered microorganisms including archaea and bacteria living near ocean rift vents. Water emerging from these vents can reach temperatures of 350 degrees Celsius or more.

Bacteria are showing us that life is possible even under these extreme conditions.

They found giant clams, eyeless shrimp, and tube worms.

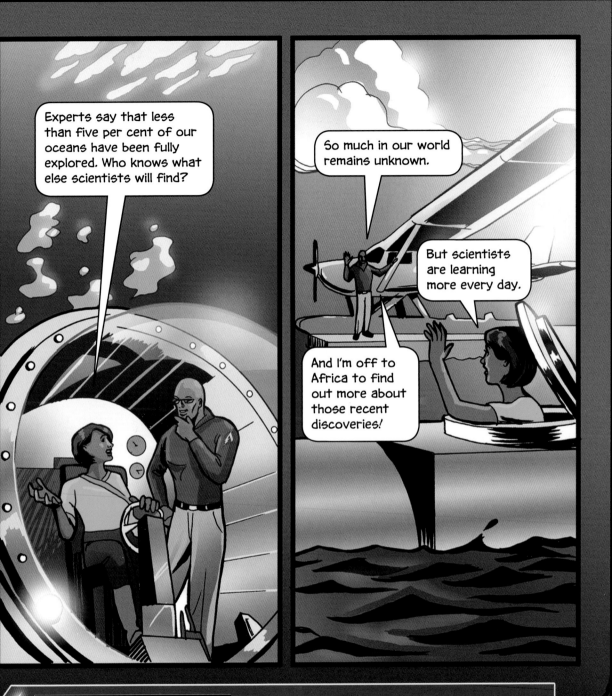

Bacteria are the ultimate survivors. They've been discovered deep under Antarctic ice, in clouds high above Earth's surface, and in the salty waters of the Dead Sea. Some bacteria don't need oxygen or sunlight to live. Based on what they're discovering, scientists are figuring out how life might survive on other planets.

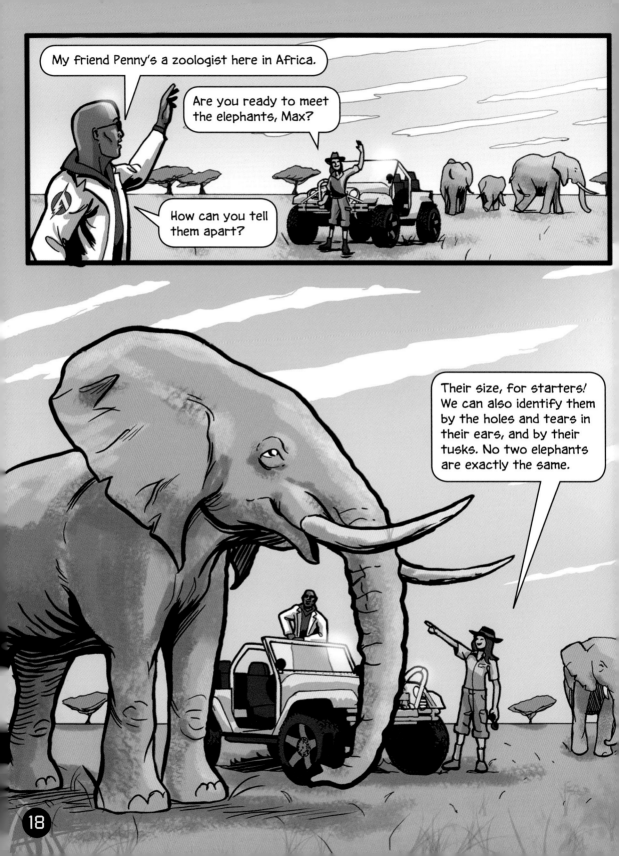

You might think that we know everything there is to know about elephants. But that's not true. Just recently, a scientist proved something new about how they communicate.

See the elephants freezing in their tracks? We think they're picking up vibrations in the ground by using their feet.

Elephants make the ground rumble with low frequency vocalizations and foot stomps. Other elephants may be able to sense these tremors through their feet.

They can use these rumbles to coordinate their movements over long distances. They also send out warnings and messages.

Look! It's Nigel.

He was expecting me. We're going virus hunting in the forest.

So tell me more about what a virologist does.

Viral vitals
A virus is a tiny bundle of chemicals covered with protein. It can only grow and multiply when it enters and takes over the cells of a living thing. Viruses cause many diseases in plants, animals, and people. Human viruses cause influenza and the common cold, as well as dangerous diseases such as polio, smallpox, and AIDS.

Virologists study viruses. Some viruses can cause deadly diseases. We think it's only a matter of time before an outbreak of a new disease strikes. I want to help predict what it will be.

Outbreaks of new viral diseases usually begin with animals. Sometimes a virus from an animal changes in a way that allows it to infect a human.

Right. HIV — the virus that causes AIDS — and swine flu began in animals before they infected humans.

I go to the places where humans and wild animals live together. I want to find where and when the viruses leap from one species to another.

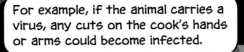

For example, if the animal carries a virus, any cuts on the cook's hands or arms could become infected.

I get hunters to collect drops of blood from the animals they've killed. We study the blood to see what viruses the animals are carrying.

We also take blood samples from the hunters and their families. The samples will show me if they've been exposed to any new viruses.

Identifying new viruses gives us a chance to create vaccines to control them. It might not be easy for a scientist to find a new species of elephant, but we find new viruses every year.

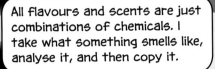

All flavours and scents are just combinations of chemicals. I take what something smells like, analyse it, and then copy it.

I even try to improve the scents. Smell these strips.

This is amazing. It smells just like fresh strawberry. This one smells like strawberry jam, and the next one smells like strawberry ice cream.

Now I'm hungry for a strawberry sundae! But I still have one last appointment back home.

It's all in the chemicals, Max. I've created hundreds of different smells. They're used in foods, sweets, household products, and perfumes.

Forensic scientists help solve mysteries by collecting and analysing physical evidence taken from a crime scene. What kind of crime-fighting science are you using today, Adele?

Some people use science to solve mysteries in nature. Others use it to solve actual crimes.

POLICE

I'm working on a robbery case right now. Let's go to the scene of the crime.

The victim fought with the robber. He tore the robber's jacket, which means we have a fabric sample to analyse.

And it looks like we might even have a sample of the robber's blood.

I'm also looking for fingerprints and palm prints.

I tag, log, and package any evidence I find. Later I'll analyse the evidence in the crime lab. If the robber's fingerprints are on file, we should be able to find him.

When you get to the fair, give me an update.

I hope you catch the robber!

25

Well, I think it's working. The children seem really interested in science.

It's no wonder. Finding out new things is the most exciting thing on Earth!

MORE ABOUT SCIENTISTS

Climatologists drill down thousands of metres to remove cores of ice from ancient glaciers. They look for bubbles of air trapped inside. The air tells them the levels of different gases found in the ancient atmosphere. Scientists now know that today's air is choked with carbon dioxide gas, which causes global warming. The atmosphere has around 30 times more carbon dioxide than at any time in the past 800,000 years. By 2100, levels may be higher than in the past 10 million years.

Vaccines boost the immune system's natural ability to protect itself from disease-causing germs and even abnormal or diseased cells. Scientists have already created a few vaccines to help prevent and treat certain types of cancer. Researchers today are looking for safe and effective vaccines for a variety of illnesses, including diabetes, AIDS, and Alzheimer's disease.

Forensic scientists help solve crimes. Wildlife forensic scientists help solve crimes, too – but in this case, the victim is an animal. Wildlife forensic cases often involve poachers. Scientists examine items such as blood and tissue samples, bones, teeth, fur, feathers, and stomach contents. Using what they find, they can determine what caused the animal's death.

Palaeontologists study the remains of ancient plants and animals. Those remains, called fossils, tell us what life was like long ago.

Scientists called archaeologists try to learn about the past. These scientists study ancient civilizations. They search the globe to find out what people ate, what kinds of tools they used, and what their daily lives were like.

Astronomers study the universe outside Earth's atmosphere, including moons, comets, planets, stars, and galaxies. Some astronomers study how galaxies form. Others look for signs of life outside our planet or try to figure out how the universe itself came to be.

Scientists called physicists study the tiniest particles known in the universe. All matter is made of atoms. Atoms can be broken down into even tinier particles, such as protons, neutrons, electrons, and quarks. Physicists smash these tiny particles together in huge machines called particle accelerators. This helps physicists learn more about why the universe looks and acts the way it does.

MORE ABOUT

Real name: Maxwell J. Axiom
Home town: Seattle, USA
Height: 1.86 m   **Weight:** 87 kg
Eyes: Brown   **Hair:** None

Super capabilities: Super intelligence; able to shrink to the size of an atom; sunglasses give x-ray vision; lab coat allows for travel through time and space.

Origin: Since birth, Max Axiom seemed destined for greatness. His mother, a marine biologist, taught her son about the mysteries of the sea. His father, a nuclear physicist and volunteer park warden, schooled Max on the wonders of the earth and sky.

One day while Max was hiking in the hills, a mega-charged lightning bolt struck him with blinding fury. When he awoke, he discovered a new-found energy and set out to learn as much about science as possible. He travelled the globe studying every aspect of the subject. Then he was ready to share his knowledge and new identity with the world. He had become Max Axiom, Super Scientist.

GLOSSARY

archaea group of single-celled organisms. Archaea are similar to bacteria and often live in extreme environments.

bacteria one-celled, microscopic living things that exist all around you and inside you. Many bacteria are useful, but some cause disease.

control group group of test subjects not being treated. In an experiment, the control group is used to compare scientific results against a group that is treated.

dropwindsonde device that scientists drop into hurricanes and tropical storms to measure and study them

evidence information, items, and facts that help prove something is true or false

gravity force that pulls objects with mass together. Gravity pulls objects down towards the centre of Earth.

magma melted rock found under Earth's surface

magnetic field space near a magnetic body or current-carrying body in which magnetic forces can be detected

orbit path an object follows as it goes around a sun or a planet

seismometer machine used to measure earthquakes

solar storm burst of energy from the surface of the Sun. Solar storms can affect Earth's magnetic field.

submersible small underwater craft powered by motors

vaccine medicine that prevents a disease

FIND OUT MORE

Books

Great Scientists (Eyewitness), Jacqueline Fortey
(Dorling Kindersley, 2011)

National Geographic Kids: Everything Volcanoes and Earthquakes, (National Geographic Society, 2013)

Police Forensics (Radar), Adam Sutherland
(Wayland, 2013)

The Scientists Behind (series) (Raintree, 2011)

Scientists in the Field (series) (Houghton Mifflin Harcourt)

Websites

pbskids.org/dragonflytv/scientists/index.html
Learn about the lives of real scientists on this website.

www.planet-science.com
Visit the Planet Science website for science information, activities, games and much more!

www.sciencenewsforkids.org
Visit this website to stay up to date with all the latest news in the world of science.